Scouse United's Daniel Team

By

John Fagan.

Illustrations by Malcolm Young.

Lou and Tich, back page illustration Rikey Austin.

Graphic Design by Ken Hatton.

All profits from the sale of this book will be donated to Claire House Hospice, St John's Hospice, Clatterbridge and Zoe's place, Liverpool

Other books published by the author

Two up, Two Down.
The Other Fella.
Spots Pimples and Bum fluff.
(An apprentice tale)
West Kirby Banter.

Contact….e.mail johnfagan356@yahoo.co.uk

Acknowledgements

Ken Hatton, good friend and neighbour. His enthusiasm and computer skills have

been a great help in producing the book.

Malcolm Young whose illustrations and drawings enhance my writing so much.

John and Paula Fowler for their proof reading expertise..

Bill Cliff, for his photograph input.

Rikey Austin, artist of Moments in Time, Card Toppers.

Michael, and staff at Wilson's chemist West Kirby for promoting my previous books.

Copyright © 2012 John Fagan

A catalogue record for this book is available from the British Library

ISBN 978-1-62407-423-3

Preface

It was my friend and local author John Fowler who suggested I put pen to paper and write a light hearted account of his beloved Everton. To make it different, he suggested I write it in verse. It soon became obvious, however, that without including the red half of the City, I'd struggle to find a way of portraying the book in the style I anticipated. Consequently, the fictitious Driscoll family were introduced to enhance the tale.

John's collection of memorabilia, including numerous scrapbooks, magazines and programmes from the forties and fifties era provided a tremendous source of information as I ploughed through the statistic side of the task. The newspaper and magazine 'cuttings' of long forgotten heroes were also a joy to read.

Drawing from an original photo. by Bert Hardy.

Bill and Jim, the Driscoll twins

Introduction

I'm known as Danny Driscoll, an advocate of dreams,

I've been a dreamer all my life, it's in the blood it seems.

The first game I remember, before the age of ten.

Dad taking me to Goodison Park standing in the pen.

We were playing Man United, I was four foot four,

I leapt above my rivals, to level up the score.

With thumbs behind my braces, I swaggered home with Dad,

my name was being chanted, the crowd were going mad.

'Who is the kid who scored that goal?' the fans were all aglow,

'Cannonball Danny Driscoll,' I was keen to let them know.

I couldn't wait to tell me Mam, she took it in her stride,

'Well done son,' was all she said, I'd hoped she'd show more pride.

I then became a dreamer, was noted near and far,

I followed the Blues to every ground by super jet or car.

Sometimes I defended, or was needed on the wing,

'The Golden Vision' had no chance when I was in full swing.

And it wasn't only football, that kept my mind at ease,

I'd close my eyes and off I'd go to Kingdoms overseas.

My rank would be ambassador and fly the Union Jack,

then visit all our embassies with the diplomatic pack.

In China or America I was treated with respect,

they thought I was the Bees'n' Knees, with my Mersey dialect.

I told them of our two great teams, and the Beatles contribution,

and how to make a pan of scouse, a culinary constitution.

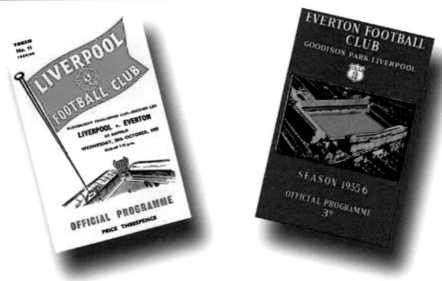

… continued from page 2.

Of course there's many things in life that are sad and often tragic,
a welcome hand, a friendly heart, some need a touch of magic.
Yet, a gift we've all inherited is called imagination,
It's given free to everyone despite their rank or station.

If you want to be a super star, or fly to outer space,
then close your eyes, relax a while, forget the rodent race.
Just imagine there's a massive store, with stacks of unclaimed dreams,
help yourself to what you wish, it's cheaper than it seems.

Then off you go enjoy the ride, may you find the trip a pleasure,
with all your worries locked away, sit back enjoy the leisure.
But keep away from Goodison Park 'til the Blues have sold their shares,
when you return, they could be owned, by a flamboyant millionaire.

And so it's back to basics, and why I wrote this book,
these albums are a true account of what players gave and took.
They were driven by the will to win and please their loyal faithful,
with skill and fancy ball control, well known for being graceful.

My grandson loves to visit us, he likes to hear the crack,
and though I try to wind him up, he soaks up all the flack.
I promised that we'd clear the loft where memories are stored,
they've been up there for years on end it's time they were explored.

...when he asked if I could reach the loft,
it seemed a trifle high...

Treasure in the loft

I was staying at my grandad's place one weekend last July,

when he asked if I could reach the loft, it seemed a trifle high.

He had cartons full of programmes and scrapbooks from the past,

so I climbed up on a wobbly chair as a sailor scales a mast.

The nearest box was decked in blue the others coloured red,

I slipped them down to grandpa, which he balanced on his head.

He spread them out with utmost care across the kitchen table,

well aware one leg was short and the other three unstable.

'Half' he said, belonged to Dad, the rest were Bill's possessions,

he was my Dad's twin brother, and football their obsession.

The dust removed, lids undone, we opened up this treasure,

there were programmes fifty-odd years old, and verses for our pleasure.

The contents in the first box, told the story of the Blues,

with dates of epic derby games, and the newspaper reviews.

History was recorded, in a neat and steady hand,

I felt so proud to read accounts and tried to understand,

why Uncle Bill despised the blues, while dad was quite the fan,

was Uncle Bill a rebel, or a poor deluded man.

As Grandpa was an expert, of both our premier teams,

I seized the opportunity, to see what I could glean.

I asked about the written verse, hoping he'd explain,

'A gift from my old man,' he said,' passed down the Driscoll chain.'

... a searing pain would shoot right down to comfort
and twist your face...

The old leather casey

8

'What about those caseys, Gramp, were they very hard to kick?
'It depended if you caught them right, they were difficult to flick.
But footy boots had metal caps to give the toes protection,
leather studs nailed underneath, were given strict inspection.

In winter when the ground was wet, and you went up for a header,
you'd tend to count your lucky stars if you missed it altogether.
But if, by chance, your forehead came in contact with the lace,
a searing pain would shoot right down to contort and twist your face.

Now these yarns I aim to tell you Tom have come from dear old Dad,
they can be taken with a pinch of salt, it's up to you m'lad.
Dad was keen on fairy tales, to keep us all amused,
but often on a Saturday night, we all had different views.

...The Chinese, of course, devised their own game...

Bladdered

A pig's bladder, young Tom, was a popular ball,
blown up and booted by the short and the tall.
They were hoofed in the streets, jiggers, back yards,
and over the years were mentioned by Bards.

The Chinese, of course, devised their own game,
a system so easy, other folk tried to claim.
It was based on twelve peasants, using their skill,
by lobbing a bladder over the nearest steep hill.

Their feet were like lightning controlling a bladder,
that was faster and sharper than a sinuous adder.
The pitch had no boundaries, they weren't bothered who won,
it was part of their leisure, just playing for fun.

After being inflated, there was something quite odd,
a face had been painted like some mythical god.

The great Ball of China

In a remote part of China many centuries ago,

a huge cow was slaughtered with a perfect timed blow.

The feast was prepared in traditional fashion,

and the locals were fed with a stew made with passion.

Removing the bladder seemed to take ages,

it was pleated and folded like a book with large pages.

After being inflated there was something quite odd,

a face had been painted like a mythical god.

News of the bladder spread out far and wide,

as pilgrims swarmed in from the vast countryside.

The large ball was sacred the elders decided,

after checking strange words which were written lopsided.

It was taken for safety to far off Tibet,

but captured by bandits, who were always a threat.

Nothing was heard for a number of years,

then someone reported a face on a sphere.

It appeared to be smiling, like the man on the moon,

bobbing around during a heavy monsoon.

It was spotted in India, Burma and Spain,

and flew over Egypt during the great Caesar's reign.

Across oceans and forests it continued its mission,

even entered a mosque without getting permission.

It was said to have trawled into Eskimo space,

parading round icebergs with smoothness and grace.

… continued from page 12.

It carried on floating away from the East,
drifted to Plymouth during Sir Francis Drake's feast.
It cast a huge shadow as he was about to take aim,
so he brought out a cannon and ignited the flame.

He blasted six shots in rapid succession,
two hit the target, four made no impression.
The balls didn't have any effect on the bladder,
as the shots hurtled back like a strike from an adder.

The bladder was supple with skin like elastic,
and for Drakes merry men the outcome was drastic.
They fled from the green in sheer desperation,
and lost all respect for protecting the nation.

As years drifted by the sightings diminished,
it was taken for granted the bladder was finished.
When a mid summer's storm flooded Dublin's fair city,
a huge ball appeared, looking battered and gritty.

Now McGinty lived local, he was a kindly old soul,
after a skin full at Hearty's, took his usual stroll.
But those eight pints of Guinness affected his brain,
so he rested his bones in a cold country lane.

A few minutes past seven he opened one eye,
his tongue felt like leather and mouth was bone dry.
He glanced at the heavens, no sign of the stars,
caught sight of the bladder and thought it was Mars.

...Tony Mac was a con-man - sharper than most...

.... continued from page 14.

When the face began smiling, he was up on his feet,
took off like a rocket, white as a sheet.
He dashed into Hearty's his eyes open wide,
'I've just seen the divil, be Jasus,' he cried.

The bladder set sail again crossing the sea,
was seen by the Liver Birds near the Albert dock quay.
The Mersey was murky, conditions were poor,
it was dragged by the tide to the Cast Iron Shore.

Tony Mac was a con man - sharper than most,
who spent his spare time at this foul patch of coast.
He spotted the bladder stuck firm in the mud,
with a message in Chinese, the omens looked good.

Most of the Dingle knew Mac was discreet,
as he carried his loot up a back terrace street.
In his ma's double tin bath, he scrubbed off the scale,
the face on the bladder was distinctively pale.

He pushed his small barrow down hill towards town,
the side streets were empty in old Chinatown.
He'd heard on the grapevine of Mister.J.Wang,
a master of magic and Tiddlywink twang.

Mister Wang was enthralled by the work of the scribe,
for he knew all about the mysterious tribe.
And soon he deciphered the message with ease,
it was logged in a notebook, for his fellow Chinese.

...Researching the bladder became a priority...

…continued from page 16.

Then questions were raised by eminent teachers,

why the skin on the bladder had unusual features.

How did it float - with what type of gas?

and where was the teat to inflate all the mass.

After weeks of dissecting they were still none the wiser,

so decided to wait for the local advisor.

The bladder it seemed was of sources divine,

Mister Wang had the answer, he would reveal in due time.

Researching the bladder became a priority,

it was weighted with lead in a secret laboratory.

The dynamics were tested, results pretty good,

with the hide stitched in sections held the model like wood.

A teat was developed with a tongue and a lace,

while the leather prevented it floating in space.

The casey, though smaller was an instant success,

but without Mack's quick thinking, they'd have been in a mess.

As football developed, strict rules were applied,

each team had a total of eleven a side.

Across cities and townships the casey was praised,

which began life in China when a huge cow was braised.

But what was the message Mister Wang found compelling,

when decoded in English had unusual spelling.

Have faith and be patient, each word he'll disclose,

the writing, though faded, will be finally exposed.

... by men who were blessed with the gift of
hindsight...

From a seed to a giant

A man of the cloth, and sportsman to boot,
Ben Chambers from Shepley, was keen and astute.
Now, cricket was always the sport of the wealthy,
so he introduced football more cheaper and healthy.

St Domingo's F.C was a Sunday school team,
from humble beginnings, came the Everton dream.
A small seed was planted in the Queen's Head one night,
by men who were blessed with the gift of hindsight.

They seized the potential, put forward a plan,
as the tree sprouted branches history began.
Everton soon prospered were revered far and wide,
predicted by many as a future top side.

Victoria was monarch, in the year seventy eight,
by the end of her reign, Everton were in a fine shape.
The club turned professional and believe it or not,
played their football at Anfield, before the Reds' nabbed the spot.

But, a dispute arose over increase in rent,
so the team packed their bags to express their dissent.
They crossed Stanley Park to continue their trade,
at a magnificent new stadium reputations were made.

The move was a winner, full gates every week,
players were skilful, active and sleek.
Goodison's culture was ranked with the best,
according to critics knocked spots off the rest.

A man of the cloth, and sportsman
to boot,
Ben Chambers from Shepley, was
keen and astute...

In the beginning.

Those who remained revealed their intention,
to make Liverpool F.C worthy of mention.
The first derby played, was like two teams at war,
the Blues were outstanding, three nil was the score.

I suppose it was then that keen rivalry began,
to outsmart each other was the obvious plan.
Families divided, a choice between two,
you were either a Red nose or baptised a Blue.

Royal blue was the choice of the Everton team,
success an advantage for enticing top cream.
Great players arrived, pioneers of the game,
men who were proud of the Goodison name.

The Reds took much longer to reach such acclaim,
but slowly and surely climbed the ladder of fame.
By the end of the decade 'The Pool' had arrived,
they played clever football and easily survived.

THIS famous club, like many others, originated from youthful members of a church group, in this case, those of St. Domingo Congregational Church, Everton. There had been a cricket club attached to this church for many years prior to 1878, the year church members decided to launch St. Domingo's Football Club, later to become famous as Everton F.C.

The first games of St. Domingo's were purely friendly affairs played at Stanley Park against local elevens, no "gate" money being taken.

In 1879 a general meeting was held at the Queen's Head Hotel in Village Street (at that time, the club's headquarters) and very close to Ye Ancient Everton Toffee House. As a result of this meeting, St. Domingo's F.C. became known as Everton. On December 23, 1879, they played their first game under this new name and defeated St. Peter's eleven.

Two years later in 1880-81, Everton became members of the Lancashire Football Association, their first away game being against Great Lever (Near Bolton), and after a drawn game, were routed by eight goals to one! In 1882, the club rented

Plot of land

In addition to being a successful businessman, this gentleman was also a keen sportsman, and offered the club a plot of land in Anfield Road, Liverpool (later to become the home of Liverpool F.C.). Everton used this ground for nine years, their first game there resulted in a 5-0 success over Earlstown, and once again they won the "local" trophy by defeating Bootle in the final. A report of this match states that rivalry existing between these two clubs, makes the present day rivalry between Everton and Liverpool appear "very tame."

In the F.A. Cup Draw of 1887-8, the "Toffee men" (as they were now firmly tagged) were drawn against Bolton Wanderers at Pike Lane in the first round. Everton were beaten 1-0, but protested against Wanderers centre-forward Struthers. The protest was upheld, the clubs met again on no less than four occasions before Everton won by 2-1. This time it was the turn of Wanderers to protest, claiming that Everton had broken the rules of Professionalism by offering certain players jobs outside football as inducements to sign on. The club were found guilty, suspended for a month, and seven players declared professionals.

from a Mr. Cruitt, a field located in Priory Road, and their first gate realised the princely sum of 13/-.

One year later (1883-4), the club succeeded in winning their first trophy, the Liverpool and District F.A. Cup, defeating Earlstown by 1-0 in the final. As the critics of the time remarked, due to this success, Everton began to command a big following, and this fact was noted by an Alderman James Houlding, a former Lord Mayor of Liverpool.

Due to the demands of Lancashire clubs, who were instrumental in seeking the birth of professionalism, which became legalised in 1885, Everton were among the first to adopt this code.

The club's first two professionals were George Dobson and George Farmer, and the following season the club signed their first player from Scotland, full-back Alec Dick, whom they secured from Kilmarnock.

Up for the cup.

At the turn of the century the Blues held their own,

in 1906 the cup returned home.

Crystal Palace, the venue, full to the brim,

shoulder to shoulder, supporters crammed in.

The Blues versus Newcastle, we were on the attack,

a fine goal was scored by the Everton pack.

The blow sealed the fate for a Geordie retreat,

who quickly conceded a one goal defeat.

The heroes that day were treated like royalty,

as the team won the hearts of the fans with their loyalty.

The trophy was ours - brought back to the Mersey,

then placed in a cabinet with the clubs famous jersey.

Thousands of fans were out on the street,

oceans of blue celebrated their fete.

Lime Street was buzzing, St George's packed tight,

players applauded as they came into sight.

The popular Scott defended the sticks,

Balmer and Crelly created neat tricks.

Makepeace and Abbott, covered miles without tiring,

Taylor was captain, classy, inspiring.

Jack Sharp on the right wing, Hardman the left,

no one was faster, skilful or deft.

Bolton and Settle controlled the mid field,

not many made progress, as they faced a blue shield.

DISAPPOINTING "FINAL" FOOTBALL.

Everton Win Deservedly After a
Poor Game—Newcastle Players
Nervous and Slow.

EVERTON, 1 ; NEWCASTLE, 0.

In Doleful Memory

OF

EVERTON,

WHO FELL

Fighting for the Cup.

—

When shall we be in London town
Sing my laddies, oh !
Not this year for we are down,
Sing my laddies, oh !

HAPPY CHRISTMAS
FIRST FOR PRESTON

The First League match to be played on
Christmas Day took place in 1889
When Preston, the reining champion, beat
Aston Villa 3-2. After that Preston never
Looked back and went on to retain the
League title.

One Halfpenny.   MONDAY, APRIL 22, 1907

SHEFFIELD WEDNESDAY WIN THE FINAL CUP-TIE FINAL.

World Cup 1966

WORLD CUP MATCHES Goodison Park, Liverpool, 4
TUESDAY, 12th JULY AT 7.30 p.m. BULGARIA v. BRAZIL
FRIDAY, 15th JULY AT 7.30 p.m. BRAZIL v. HUNGARY
TUESDAY, 19th JULY AT 7.30 p.m. PORTUGAL v. BRAZIL
SATURDAY, 23rd JULY AT 3.00 p.m. QUARTER FINAL
MONDAY, 25th JULY AT 7.30 p.m. SEMI-FINAL

What's on in Liverpool

10th JULY to 31st JULY

…continued from page 24.

Sandy Young in the middle, scored the critical goal,
led Everton's line up, played a pivotal role.
The following year we defended our title,
to keep a clean sheet was deemed to be vital.
Sheffield Wednesday were strong, and beat us two one,
eighty thousand agreed that the best team had won.

1915, for us, was another great season,
standards were higher - good football the reason.
By the last week of April, we were champs once again,
opponents were crushed like a sack full of grain.

A photo was taken of the Blues winning team,
the Toffees were jubilant having full filled a dream.
Tom Fleetwood, Al Grenyer, Bob Thomo, Jim Galt,
Maconnachie, and Makepeace, Tom Fern earned their salt.

The master, Sam Chedzoy, adored for his skill,
Kersopp, played inside, rarely stayed still.
Bob Parker, James Roberts, and the speedy Clennell,
who'd be now worth a fortune, if we had them to sell.

Imagine today's stars compared to those greats,
carrying goal posts to the pitch with their mates.
Joining spectators on the way to the game,
working class heroes, not bothered by fame.

Shanks's pony for transport or clattering trams,
enjoying the crack with knowledgeable fans.
The passion of match days, spirits raised high,
moments of pleasure, money just couldn't buy.

… continued from page 26.

Fans in great numbers, banter all round,

excitement, sheer magic, as they entered the ground.

And you wouldn't believe what some of them brought,

old chairs to stand on for those who were short.

It must have been chaos if perched off the floor,

as the surge of the crowd met the Goodison roar.

Swept off your feet by a powerful rush,

hands shielding ribs from the inevitable crush.

Spun in a circle, trying to stay calm,

then back were you started without doing much harm.

This was a fine English team, 1922: Back row, left to right: Osborne (Fulham), Moss (Aston Villa), Taylor (Huddersfield), Grimsdell (Tottenham), Harrow (Chelsea). Front row: Mercer (Sheffield), Smith (W.B.A.), Seed (Tottenham), Wilson (Sheffield W.), Chambers (Liverpool), William (Clapton O.)

IN THE OLD days the Off-Side Rule was known as sneaking! Boys, we are told, used to sneak around in among the enemy and wait for their own side to kick the ball their way.

Eton College Rules a hundred years ago put it plainly: 'A player is considered to be sneaking when only three or less than three of the opposite side are before him and the ball is behind him; in such a case he may not kick the ball'.

To-day the Off-Side Rule plays a vital part in the game. It should be known to every player. So read Law Eleven carefully and then take the tests. Correct solutions are given at the foot of page 103.

Time to reflect

'Now then Tommy me lad, let's stop for a brew,

give Grandma a shout, a cuppa tea's overdue.

Help yourself to a biscuit, while I nip to the back,

then I'll continue the story, unless you want a quick snack.'

But Tommy declined, he was keen to know more,

there was so much to learn from this old secret store.

'Where about were we up to? Old Dan scratched his head,

as he flicked through a diary and pages he'd read.

They were written in long hand with a fine pen and ink,

every letter was perfect including each link.

Gran brought in the tea pot and glanced at her hubby,

half moons on his pecker, face rosy and chubby.

He was back in his hey days enjoying the trip,

comparing life's journey, like he'd sailed it by ship.

But, Gran had a secret, held close to her chest,

in her heart she was Red, but had kept it suppressed.

With three in the family all football fanatics,

she sat on the fence it was far less traumatic.

...a ball was produced and a challenge arranged...

1914 - 18 War.

As Dan sipped his cuppa and relaxed in his chair,
with eyelids half closed pictured his father's despair.
He was writing of warfare so his children would know,
how those poor souls had suffered, many decades ago.

Soon Dan was dreaming, his mouth open wide,
of battles and trenches with nowhere to hide.
A chosen outsider looking in from above,
witnessing hatred, no kindness nor love.

He watched the beginning in nineteen fourteen,
with thousands of lads grasping unfinished dreams.
Straight into trenches without time for a prayer,
mowed down like fodder - for loved ones despair.

He remembered a tale, still fresh in his mind,
raised everyone's spirits and hope for mankind.
It was agreed by both parties for a truce to take place,
at Christmas adversaries would come face to face.

Weapons discarded, troops greeted foes,
shared meagre possessions from damp muddy clothes.
A ball was produced, a challenge arranged,
the young fit and healthy joined in the exchange.

The teams played with vigour, light tackles, clean fun,
some fell in a heap after a hundred yard run.
Language no problem, the object compete,
it ended up even, both squads had sore feet.

FINED FOR WEAK TEAMS

IN 1924 Newcastle United were found to have fielded very weak teams in seven League matches before they went to Wembley for the Cup Final and the Football Association imposed a record fine of £750 on them. Arsenal were fined £250 on a similar charge some twelve seasons later.

J. BALMER
(Liverpool)

Cash savers

GOALKEEPERS in Morocco get a reward of ten shillings each time they make a good save. Really good 'keepers stand a chance of earning anything up to £6 a game!

BILLY Meredith scored his first goal at St. James's Park, against Newcastle, in 1894—he scored his 200th goal on October 12, 1907, on the same ground.

In Dixie's best-ever team Elisha Scott (above) is his choice in goal. "There is no argument about it—he is unchallenged in that position," says Dean.

● In 1923 a little man named Hugh Gallacher came into prominence with the Airdrieonians. He was too small, they said, to be a centre-forward. Ask Newcastle United, ask Chelsea, ask Scotland!

Ask the cowardly people who, aware that they could not beat him by fair means, goaded him with insulting remarks, knowing that this incredibly clever footballer had a rather short temper.

It was a privilege to have been able to see him play so many times.

The strike in 1920 fizzled out

STRIKE! That six-letter word has been used so often in post-war industrial Britain that it was almost inevitable it would enter the football vocabulary with a vengeance.

But it is by no means new to the game in this country.

Forty years ago the Players' Union asked its members to come out on strike in order to negotiate improved standards of pay and bonus monies.

But this 1920 action was a fiasco. For one thing, it happened during the summer "close season" months when football's impact was at its lowest ebb.

The idea originally was for players who had been retained by their clubs at the end of that season to refuse to re-sign until better terms were forthcoming.

Many players did this, but it lasted for only two weeks, and then fizzled out when the majority of players decided to accept the existing terms and re-signed. Those who did try to prolong the situation reluctantly signed on again when they were unable to support themselves or their families.

In isolated cases, clubs have gone on strike for domestic reasons, although there are no longer any in the League today.

It has been a common occurrence in South America where certain Argentinian club players have refused to play just before kick-off time unless financial improvements were made.

But there are relatively few strikes today in those countries where wages and bonuses are among the highest in the world.

In Africa, a team went on strike and refused to play because of interference by a local witch doctor. But that is another story . . .

… continued from page 32.

A whistle shrilled loudly, troops sloped from the pitch,
sand bags lay scattered, behind a long muddy ditch.
Carols were sung at the end of the day,
then back to the trenches to kneel down and pray.

Dan stirred for a moment and opened his eyes,
he turned to young Tommy, he could still hear the cries.
'It was grim for those youngsters, when you weigh up the score,
they didn't want conflict, or conscripted for war.'

The youth of these nations weren't given a chance,
paid the ultimate sacrifice and sent over to France.'

Football resumed after almost four years,
it was back to the grind bringing sadness and tears.
Each town had its heroes, who sacrificed lives,
fatherless children and heartbroken wives.

TOKEN
No. 11
1959/60

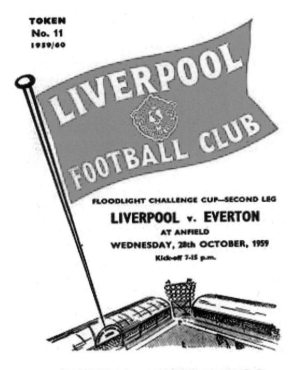

FLOODLIGHT CHALLENGE CUP—SECOND LEG

LIVERPOOL v. EVERTON

AT ANFIELD

WEDNESDAY, 28th OCTOBER, 1959

Kick-off 7-15 p.m.

OFFICIAL PROGRAMME

PRICE THREEPENCE

LIVERPOOL v. EVERTON

Right   LIVERPOOL (Red Jerseys)   Left

RUDHAM (1)

MOLYNEUX (2)   MORAN (3)

WHEELER (4)   NICHOLSON (5)   TWENTYMAN (6)

BIMPSON (7)   MELIA (8)   HARROWER (10)   A'COURT (11)

HUNT (9)

HICKSON (9)

SHACKLETON (11)   COLLINS (10)   THOMAS (8)   HARRIS (7)

HARRIS, B. (6)   JONES (5)   KING (4)

BRAMWELL (3)   PARKER (2)

DUNLOP (1)

Left   EVERTON (Blue Jerseys)   Right

Referee: Mr. F. V. Stringer (Liverpool)
Linesmen: Mr. D. L. Lovelady (Red Flag)
Mr. A. Edge (Yellow Flag)

Billy's red box.

Dan sighed as he gathered his other lads things,
before carefully tugging the waxen type string.
'We'll go through our Bills stuff, just to be fair,
although he was Red, it will show that we care.'

There were diaries and scrapbooks with programmes galore,
poems he had written about his teams final score.
His writing was perfect no smudges or stains,
no one could doubt that the lad used his brains,

Liverpool's history, Dan had to admit,
was littered with trophies, since the acrimonious split.
John Houlding gained credit when forming the club,
but for Everton directors, it was a definite snub.

After years of resentment, the teams settled down,
the Reds' stayed at Anfield, the Blues nearer town.
Both were successful in league and the cup.
at J.Houlding's funeral, former colleagues turned up.

Dan glanced at his grandson, who was like his son Jim,
quiet disposition, big hearted and thin.
The years had flown by, since Jim passed away,
he had a lump in his throat as he remembered that day.

He thought about match days, the bustling crowd,
the lads teasing each other good humoured and loud.
Flicking and passing, or trying to dribble,
as he strode between them commanding the middle.

EVERTON

Right · · · Left

LEYLAND (1)

MOORE (2) · TANSEY (3)

FARRELL (4) · JONES (5) · LELLO (6)

McNAMARA (7) · WAINWRIGHT (8) · FIELDING (10) · HARRIS, B. (11)

HARRIS. J. (9)

___

Referee :

Mr. R. H. Mann

(Worcester)

Linesmen :

Messrs.: J. H. Hemmingway

(Yellow Flag)

and R. J. Fryer (Red Flag)

BENTLEY (9)

BLUNSTONE (11) · TINDALL (10) · McNICHOL (8) · J. LEWIS (7)

SAUNDERS (6) · LIVINGSTONE (5) · NICHOLAS (4)

WILLEMSE (3) · SILLETT (2)

THOMSON (1)

Left · Right

CHELSEA

… continued from page 36.

Jim dressed in blue, Billy bright red,

swinging their rattles would waken the dead.

Pubs spilling over, punters three deep,

last orders at two - before the clock went to sleep.

Along major roads you could taste the devotion,

and under the Mersey trains rattled in motion.

Special buses were waiting to ferry the fans,

the atmosphere bristling with boisterous clans.

For Derby's and cup games they were biased, of course,

if Liverpool won, Bill would be happy and hoarse.

When the Blues' took the points it would show by his mood,

he'd be out on the ale and right off his food.

But as they grew older there were signs of a change,

the banter was different, even girls they'd exchange.

On the day Billy married he wore a rosette,

his suit was bright crimson, which I'll never forget.

...he was crossed with a poodle and a big Irish hound, ... because of his breeding he wasn't quite sound...

Toffee versus Gorbal

It was Grandma who mentioned the dog known as Toffee,

who wouldn't drink water unless flavoured with coffee.

He came from the tenements, reputedly tough,

when her lad brought him home, he looked a real scruff.

Most folk in the street had a hound for protection,

each given a name, after careful selection.

Jim tied a thin rope round the dog's scraggy neck,

when they ventured outside, Toffee peed every step.

He'd done all his mating, was bony and slender,

when marking his speck, not a hint of surrender.

Bred in the south end, he was happy as Larry,

after his master had 'legged it' with all he could carry.

He was crossed with a poodle and a big Irish hound,

because of his breeding, he wasn't quite sound.

Bill didn't like him, he said he was vicious,

when the mutt chewed his match scarf he was highly suspicious.

His work mates were dying to break the bad news,

that Toffee was reared by a family of Blues.

The O'Grady's were known as odd ball fanatics,

who wouldn't use red in the house or the attic.

Then Bill was approached by his foreman at Laird's,

to nip up to Glasgow, something needed repaired.

He was a fourth year apprentice, smart at his trade,

to John Brown's large shipyard, he was told to parade.

...There were scars round his rear, where a tail should have been...
...with half an ear missing, he looked hard and mean...

...continued from page 40.

It must have been fate when he came across Gorbal,

who hung round the shipyard as though it was normal.

The lads fed him scraps, during their dinner time break,

but it was Billy he clung to for a share of his cake.

Now if ever a canine had been dealt a poor hand,

it had to be Gorbal, from Glasgow's dock land.

He was round as a barrel, his legs were too short,

ugly to look at, but the best he had fought.

There were scars round his rear, where a tail should have been,

with half an ear missing, he looked hard and mean.

His throat had been slashed and stitched with cheap twine,

but according to locals he was as strong as a lion.

He was champion scrapper for two years on the bounce,

when the cops got a tip off, they were ready to pounce.

The culprits were captured and taken to court,

and that was the end of an illegal cruel sport.

With the job now completed, Bill was all set to go.

when he peeped at old Gorbal, his heart told him no.

It didn't take long to make up his mind,

soon they were leaving the shipyard behind.

But Billy was crafty, a plan he'd concealed,

to get rid of Toffee he would later reveal.

He called at a pet shop, bought a red leash and collar,

Gorbal looked smart for less than a dollar.

BILLY LIDDELL
TESTIMONIAL MATCH

LIVERPOOL v. INTERNATIONAL XI

AT LIVERPOOL FOOTBALL GROUND, ANFIELD
WEDNESDAY, 21st SEPTEMBER, 1960
Kick-off 7.15 p.m.

Souvenir Programme—Sixpence

TOMMY YOUNGER
LIVERPOOL
&
SCOTLAND.

IT'S OUR TEAM

IN an effort to haul themselves from the bottom of the Western League North Devon club Bideford introduced a new method of team selection. The players were invited to pick the team.

Result—Bideford have now relinquished bottom place with a 4-2 win over highly-placed Yeovil.

DAVE HICKSON

JOHN WHEELER

…. continued from page 42.

They arrived at the 'Pool a few minutes past four,
his mam almost fainted when she opened the door.
She fled to the kitchen, locked the door to the yard,
where Toffee lay snoring, instead of on guard.

'What d'yer call that?' she yelled, trembling with fear,
but Bill kept on stroking, Gorbal's dodgy half ear.
When Toffee's wet nose sniffed the scent of the stranger,
he didn't need telling he was in mortal danger.

He growled like a bear whose tail was on fire,
so Bill had no option, but gracefully retire.
They went to his Grandma's who had a spare bed,
it was just up the road amongst families of Reds.

Now this is where Gorbal came into his own,
to settle down safely and call the place home.
He established his patch after a couple of fights,
it didn't take long to sort out his rights.

When Dan trundled home after a day on the docks,
he was confronted by Mary in a deep state of shock.
She told him of Gorbal and Toffee the wimp,
he ravaged his dinner, then set off for a blimp.

It took him ten minutes to reach number nine,
his mother was normal, everything else appeared fine.
With sad doleful eyes Gorbal strolled to the door,
Dan nearly fell over when he glanced at the floor.

Mortensen, England's inside-right, makes a dangerous raid on the Irish goal in England v. Ireland match at Goodison Park, Everton, which ended in a 2-2 draw. As Mortensen heads the ball, Hinton, the Irish goalkeeper, poises himself to jump to catch it. Farrell, the right-half, beaten by Mortensen, is falling. Carey, the left back, is racing to the goalmouth to cover Hinton.

Dykes, of Scotland, and Hapgood, of England, lead their men on to the field at Wembley, prior to a War-time International.

… continued from page 44.

Gorbal's *orchestra stalls* were the biggest he'd seen,
no wonder the shock almost snuffed out his queen.
The hound wasn't bothered as they swung to and fro,
though the cobbles round Parlie lay half inch below.

Jimmy's mates were delighted, as Bill took the flak,
they called Gorbal 'big plums' just for the crack.
He was teased by the dockers a majority blue,
'Throw a cap on them lad,' was one point of view.

As the sniping continued it was getting Bill down,
so he crept to his mother's who was shopping in town.
The unsociable Toffee barely lifted his head,
as Bill moved in swiftly with a can of red lead.

The dog was stretched out on a rug near the fire,
unaware of the drama about to transpire.
Bill plastered its tail with a brush full of paint,
although badly shaken, Toffee looked rather quaint.

The commotion that followed was the talk of the town,
with Toff in the limelight, Jim was never around.
While Gorbal from Glasgow reached his highest acclaim,
he was proposed as a mascot to ensure he'd remain.

Then a designer in Ayrshire had a kilt made of tartan,
with a jock strap to match, from the folk of Dumbarton.
As proud as a peacock, Gorbal strutted his stuff,
and was famous in no time called the 'Tartan clad puff.'

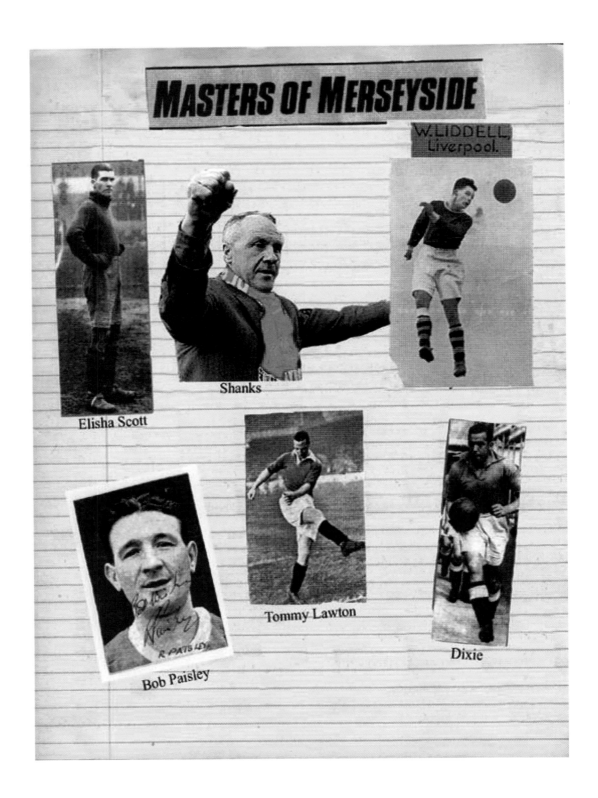

MASTERS OF MERSEYSIDE

W.LIDDELL,
Liverpool.

Shanks

Elisha Scott

Bob Paisley

Tommy Lawton

Dixie

The Reds

The Reds played at Anfield with a full team of Scots
in a friendly against Rotherham they scored with five shots.
It was the first ever match to be played at the ground,
only a handful of fans were scattered around.

Dan eased a few programmes from his son Billy's hoard,
several players were listed who struck a deep chord.
They were 'the greats' from an era he remembered quite well,
who'd worn the red jersey before the magnificent spell.

Billy Liddell was brilliant, a Scot with real class,
had a lethal left foot, was tremendously fast.
Some christened him Liddellpool, he was honest and fair,
a Justice of Peace, served the city with care.

'Here's one for the notebook,' Dan whispered to Tom,
dusting an old photo of a Methodist son.
'Parson Jim Jackson in the number three slot,
if the language turned blue he was off like a shot.'

'Now he was the greatest,' shrewd folk often said,
when goalies were mentioned who had played for the reds'.
Elisha, from Belfast, the best keeper by far,
spent a lifetime at Anfield, the red's finest star.

His clashes with Dixie were reported with relish,
their battles and passion unlikely to perish.
Dixie next morning, would don his best suit,
before boarding a tram along the West Derby route.

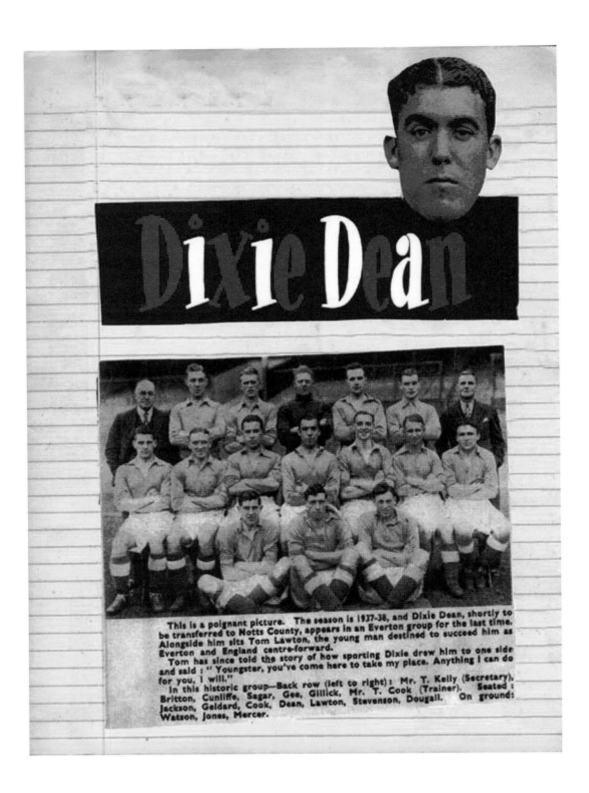

This is a poignant picture. The season is 1937-38, and Dixie Dean, shortly to be transferred to Notts County, appears in an Everton group for the last time. Alongside him sits Tom Lawton, the young man destined to succeed him as Everton and England centre-forward.

Tom has since told the story of how sporting Dixie drew him to one side and said : "Youngster, you've come here to take my place. Anything I can do for you, I will."

In this historic group—Back row (left to right): Mr. T. Kelly (Secretary), Britton, Cunliffe, Sagar, Gee, Gillick, Mr. T. Cook (Trainer). Seated : Jackson, Geldard, Cook, Dean, Lawton, Stevenson, Dougall. On ground : Watson, Jones, Mercer.

…continued from page 48.

He'd head for the chapel, where the Reds' often prayed,
rub shoulders with Elisha, if he wasn't delayed.
They'd kneel side by side on hard wooden pews,
and listened as preachers spread the good news.

At the end of the service they'd be off for a drink,
a few pints demolished, without time to think.
Not a word about football, or the Saturday game,
this was a subject, neither man entertained.

Below, the famed Everton line-up of 1928-29.—Back row (left to right) : Hart, Cresswell, Davies, Griffiths, Virr. Seated : O'Donnell, Ritchie, Forshaw, Dean, Martin, Troup.

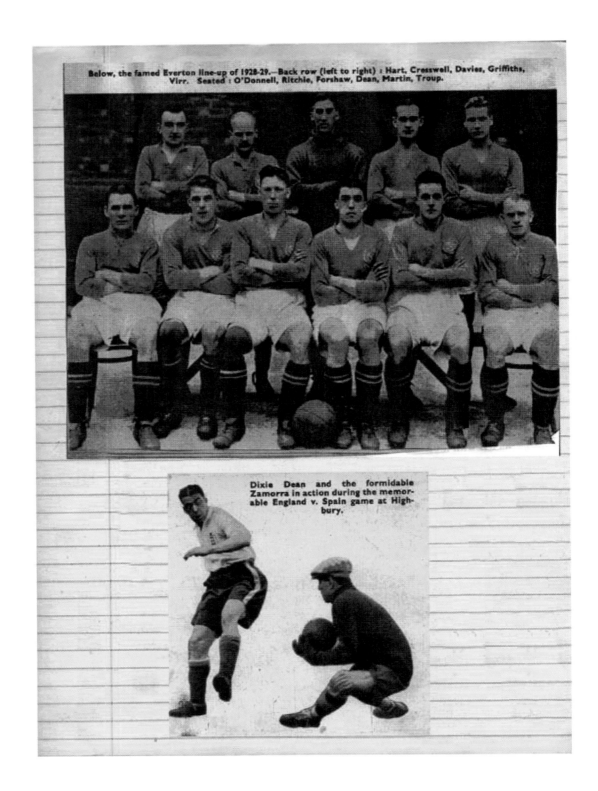

Dixie Dean and the formidable Zamorra in action during the memorable England v. Spain game at Highbury.

Give it to Dixie

He was the best centre forward the world's ever known,
the finest goal scorer, in a class of his own.
With two perfect feet - impeccably sound,
place a ball on a sixpence, anywhere in the ground.

'Give it to Dixie' rang out from the faithful,
he'd rattle the net, motivation was grateful.
Single handed he'd score, as easy as breathing,
opponents in turmoil left cursing and seething.

His humour was sharp, wicked, good fun,
when he donned the blue jersey, the game was half won.
On match days he travelled by bus, train, or tram,
adored by supporters, he was one of their clan.

Old timers remembered his sixtieth goal,
as news of the record began to unfold.
A hat trick against Arsenal in the Toffees last game,
ensured Dixie Dean entered the annals of fame.

Near the end of the thirties, a replacement was found,
the Blues sold their favourite for three thousand pounds.
He signed for Notts County played only six games,
broke a bone in his instep and was never the same.

LIVERPOOL
The Team of the Season Make League Championship History

Liverpool, Arsenal and Forest make the headlines as the trophies are handed out at the season's climax

MAY IS THE merry month for a number of clubs. It is also the season's most miserable month for the clubs who either just miss out of winning a cup or are relegated to the lower Divisions. Elsewhere in our book you will read of the season's Champions and Cup Winners . . . Again it was Liverpool, who created a new record, winning the Championship for the 11th time with a record number of points—68. Only 16 goals were put past them in their League campaign which also sets another record . . .

LEAGUE TABLES 1964-65

LEAGUE—DIVISION I
(Up to and including Saturday, 6.2.65)

	P.	W.	D.	L.	F.	A.	Pts
Leeds	29	18	6	5	55	37	42
Chelsea	28	18	6	4	62	30	42
Manchester U.	28	15	9	4	55	29	39
Tottenham	29	14	6	9	57	45	34
Nottingham F.	29	11	9	9	54	54	31
Blackburn R.	28	13	5	10	60	46	31
Liverpool	27	11	8	8	45	41	30
West Ham	28	13	4	11	57	43	30
Arsenal	29	13	4	12	51	57	30
EVERTON	27	9	11	7	48	43	29
Sheffield W.	27	10	9	8	43	37	29
Stoke C.	28	10	8	10	46	45	28
Sheffield U.	29	10	7	12	40	43	27
Leicester	28	7	11	10	54	60	25
Burnley	29	9	7	13	43	51	25
West Brom	28	7	10	11	42	44	24
Blackpool	28	8	6	14	47	57	22
Fulham	28	7	8	13	42	52	22
Birmingham C.	28	7	8	13	45	62	22
Sunderland	26	6	7	13	38	52	19
Aston Villa	26	8	2	16	32	59	18
Wolves	27	6	3	18	32	61	15

LEAGUE—DIVISION II
(Up to and including Saturday, 6.2.65)

	P.	W.	D.	L.	F.	A.	Pts
Newcastle	29	18	4	7	60	33	40
Northampton	28	13	11	4	38	31	37
Norwich	29	15	6	8	45	34	36
Bolton W.	26	14	5	7	59	37	33
Derby C.	28	12	7	9	59	51	31
Crystal P.	29	12	7	10	42	39	31
Southampton	27	10	10	7	59	44	30
Preston	29	10	10	9	52	56	30
Coventry	29	11	7	11	50	52	29
Ipswich	29	8	12	9	50	52	28
Plymouth	28	11	5	12	39	51	27
Manchester C.	28	12	3	13	46	40	27
Rotherham	26	10	6	10	49	47	26
Bury	28	9	8	11	41	42	26
Charlton	27	10	5	12	45	50	25
Middlesbrough	28	9	6	13	51	54	24
Swindon	29	11	2	16	45	59	24
Cardiff	26	7	9	10	39	39	23
Huddersfield	28	8	7	13	34	42	23
Swansea	28	7	8	13	42	55	22
Leyton	28	8	6	14	39	57	22
Portsmouth	29	7	8	14	37	56	22

…continued from page 52.

With a heart like a lion and spirit to match,

he sailed to old Ireland was a wonderful catch.

Sligo supporters swept down from the hills,

to witness a legend performing his skills.

He scored twenty seven in no time at all,

and was rightly proclaimed, 'King of football.'

The great name of Dixie has lasted through time,

just one word describes him – and that is sublime.

No good for Nelson

NELSON, despite his shrewdness, his fair-mindedness and his alertness, could never have been a referee. A referee must have good eyesight. An applicant who has lost the sight of one eye cannot be registered. Though it is now permissible to qualify and to referee if you wear spectacles, you will not be allowed to referee in Grade 1 matches unless you can manage without them and attain a minimum standard in an eyesight and colour test.

This and a thousand other tips may be found in the *F.A. Guide For Referees and Linesmen* (Heinemann, 3s. 6d.) which will be on sale this weekend. It is an official publication, well illustrated and contains innumerable test pieces with correct answers.

Stan Matthews v. Real Madrid

STANLEY Matthews is likely to play against Real Madrid next month. He has offered his services to the British Columbia All-Stars in their friendly game against the Spaniards in Vancover on August 23. His offer is likely to be snapped up.

Matthews is at present in Canada assisting the Montreal Cantalia team in the Eastern Professional League.

Gnasty Gnats

—and filthy flies
midges and mosquitoes too
keep the little buzzers off
Smooth on FLYPEL cream—it's gnew !

The new I.C.I. insect repellent, FLYPEL,
is non-greasy, doesn't show and really
works. Antiseptic too, stops any earlier
nip from going septic. Buzz off and get a
3/- tube of FLYPEL now — pests detest it !

NEW! Flypel

Flypel insect repellent cream
safe - effective - long lasting

NORTH
TERRACE
SEATS
(Uncovered)

ENTER AT TURNSTILES
(See Plan on back)

ENTRANCE

D
1

Row 12   Seat 15

EMPIRE STADIUM, WEMBLEY

The Football Association Cup Competition

FINAL TIE

SATURDAY, APRIL 29th, 1933
(Kick-off 3 p.m.)

Price 5/-
(Including Tax)

A. J. Elvin
MANAGING DIRECTOR,
Wembley Stadium Limited.

THIS PORTION TO BE RETAINED
(See Conditions on back)

DEAN SCORES GREAT GOAL FOR EVERTON :

Dixie Dean, the Everton captain, scoring a remarkable goal
(above). As Langford attempted to fist out, Dean got his
head to the ball and fell into the net after it. Right, Britton, Everton right half (white shirt), defending against Mar-
shall and Herd (No. 16), Manchester's centre forward.

The thirty three Cup final

In the golden year of thirty three the Blues were Wembley bound,

Man City local rivals, were played right off the ground.

We settled down and scored three times with style and true aggression,

a crowd of ninety thousand plus, admired our team's possession.

To stand in the stadium, cost two and a tanner,

leaving plenty of room for those swinging a banner.

Two great northern clubs of similar size,

fought an action packed final for the coveted prize.

Ted Sagar, was keeper, a talented goalie,

Warnie Cresswell adored, on par with the holy.

Cliff Britton could pass, Jock Thomson pure class,

while Cookey and Whitey covered acres of grass.

Jimmy Dunn a neat dribbler and maker of goals,

Albert Geldard, utility, could play any role.

Tommy Johnstone, Ted Critchley and the Scot, Jimmy Stein,

and then there was Dixie, the star of the team.

T. G. JONES
(Everton)

P. FARRELL,
Everton.

Tommy Eglington

E. WAINWRIGHT (Everton)

'Everton will be
title challengers
again next season'
BOB PAISLEY

'Yes, but we need two
new players to
overtake Liverpool'
GORDON LEE

My dear old Dad

'Have a doze if you're tired,' Tom said to his Gramp,
who was due forty winks, following a mild bout of cramp.
The old man responded, closed his eyes for a rest,
drifted back to the thirties, to times he knew best.

He was alongside his Father, the atmosphere tense,
opponents were Villa who had a solid defence.
When the ref blew his whistle there was a hush round the ground,
the Toffees were lucky to have reached the next round.

Dan and his father shared similar views,
and of course the main topic was always the Blues.
He joined in the banter on a Saturday night,
as they argued the toss about the wrongs and the right.

At the height of the session the subject was raised,
of the greatest team ever to merit their praise.
The old man insisted his squad led the field,
not many could argue about the stars he revealed.

He'd always relate to the thirty three team,
parading the cup which was everyone's dream.
Then he'd rattle the names to those who would listen,
and denounce all the Red lot, who by now had gone missing.

He spoke of the greats who had worn the blue jersey,
and those who made Everton the pride of the Mersey.
Top British stars with a flair for creating,
envied by clubs who had slipped down the rating.

Sagar makes sure of the ball, while Humphreys holds off two Charlton attackers.

Goal-line save by George Swindin, Arsenal goalkeeper, in the Cup Final at Wembley. Liverpool outside-right Payne, on the floor, made the effort and the other players in the picture are, left to right, Mercer, Stubbins and Les Compton

… continued from page 58.

The Toffees played football with instinctive defiance,
and Goodison was known as 'THE' school of science.
If opponents played well - a standing ovation,
respect always shown for a team's application.

Dan promised his dad he'd obey his last wish,
by placing his ashes in an earthenware dish.
Then scatter them close to the Gwladys Street Stand,
it was his last will and testament, written by hand.

After his father passed over Dan bought a blue jar,
with his 'gammy' left hand spread the ashes afar.
As he turned from the goalmouth and glanced up at the crowd,
the applause from the faithful would have made his dad proud.

'Give him a prod lad,' Gran yelled from the back.
'He'd kip on a clothes line, as long as it's slack.'
Tom gently shook Dan by his drooping left arm,
he was awake within seconds, unusually calm.

'63 Everton's 1963 League Championship line-up . . . Back (from left): Alex Parker, Jimmy Gabriel, Gordon West, Roy Vernon, Brian Labone, Mick Meagan. Front: Alex Scott, Dennis Stevens, Alex Young, Harry Catterick (manager), Derek Temple, Tony Kay.

Alan Ball

Tell me about some of your favourite players Gramp.

'Hang on for a sec lad, while I gather me wits,
I'll shake my old thinking cap, get rid of the bits.
Hundreds of players have worn the blue jersey,
and sampled the breeze from the shores of the Mersey.'

Let's start in the fifties with the Irish contingent,
Farrell, O'Neill, and Clinton were stringent.
Tommy Eglington, a winger, was as fast as a rocket,
had full backs sewn up and stuffed in each pocket.

Now, Tommy G. Jones, was a magnificent stopper,
few mastered his tackles without coming a cropper.
Another cool customer - the calm Brian Labone,
always respected whether away or at home.

Two high rated Scots, well known for their skills,
Alex Stevenson, a dribbler, Bobby Collins for thrills.
They opened defences, with a shrug or a swerve,
both of them deadly with plenty of nerve.

Colin Harvey, was clever, Dave Watson stayed cool,
Alan Ball, a great worker, Howard no fool.
Trevor Steven, a winner, Ray Wilson a star,
Peter Reid a trojan, Kevin Ratcliffe on par.

Neville Southall was solid, a rock in defence,
brimming with talent he was truly immense.
Ted Sagar's career was spoilt by the war,
highly respected, always top draw.

By Clifford Webb

FOR me and, I suppose for many other people, Goodison Park and the Everton ground will always be associated with Ireland and the Irish.

For who, among the crowd who thronged the terraces and filled the stands on September 21, 1949, can ever forget the consternation as England trooped off the field, beaten 2—o by the Republic of Ireland?

The big Irish contingent of fans went absolutely wild with joy as the final whistle blew.

In addition to the merit of a surprising victory against a very good English team, the Republic of Ireland had achieved what no other national team outside the 'home' international tournament competitors had ever been able to do—WIN ON ENGLISH SOIL.

Five years passed before Hungary visited Wembley and rubbed English football in the dust.

Amid the wailings and recriminations after that debacle, a lot of people were inclined to forget that memorable day at Goodison Park.

Everton supporters among the crowd must have viewed the 1949 match with very mixed feelings — particularly those with strong English leanings.

For that long-serving Everton favourite, Peter Farrell, helped to sink England with one of the two goals scored by the Republic of Ireland.

There was, in fact, an Everton right wing in this match—Corr and Farrell—and this pair gave Johnny Aston (Manchester United) and Jimmy Dickinson (Portsmouth), left-back and left-half respectively in the England side, a rare old run-around.

Everton's spree

I cannot ever recall so many big cheques having been signed for so many big men in so short a time as has happened now.

Tottenham Hotspur, marching in step at the head of the First Division, can field a £200,000 team. And so can Everton who, by signing 22-year-old Alex Young from Hearts for £42,000 last week, have made the R.A.S.C. private the most expensive centre-forward in Britain. Everton also paid Hearts £16,000 for Young's team-mate, left-back George Thomson.

Trace back their player expenditure since May 1958 when Falkirk's Alex Parker was signed for £18,000; September 1958—Celtic's Bobby Collins for £23,000; January 1960—Clyde's Tommy Ring for £12,000; February 1960—Wolves' Micky Lill for £15,000; Blackburn's Roy Vernon for £35,000; March 1960—Dundee's Jimmy Gabriel for £28,000; October 1960—Luton's Billy Bingham for £16,000.

And now a further £58,000 to Hearts for Young and Thomson. I make that a total of £205,000.

Yes, that was really something to remember. It pulled out all the superlatives from the national newspaper reporters (including myself!) and it hit the headlines with the biggest type then in general use.

And I think everybody was glad it happened at Goodison Park, a home of football since 1892, a ground steeped in Soccer atmosphere; just the sort of place, in fact, where football history should be written.

I am sure it will give many memories a pleasant jog if I reprint the teams of that memorable day of ten years ago. They were:

England: Williams (Wolves); Mozley (Derby), Aston (Manchester Utd.); Wright (Wolves), Franklin (Stoke), Dickinson (Portsmouth); Harris (Portsmouth), Morris (Derby), Pye (Wolves), Mannion (Middlesbrough), Finney (Preston).

Republic of Ireland: Godwin (Shamrock Rovers); Carey (Manchester Utd.), Aherne (Luton); Walsh (W.) (Manchester City), Martin (Aston Villa), Moroney (West Ham); Corr (Everton), Farrell (Everton), Walsh (D.) (West Bromwich), Desmond (Middlesbrough), O'Connor (Shamrock Rovers).

Everton had made the most of their comparatively limited space with tall, double-decker stands, ample cover all round, and viewpoints which give an intimate feeling to even the most remote spectators.

The high, brick-built outside walls of the main stand are not gems of picturesque architecture, but they certainly fit in with the surroundings.

After all, professional football was originally developed as the sport for the men from the mean streets, in the days when long journeys were out of the question for the average worker.

And so Goodison remains, a monument, if you like, to the humble beginnings of a great game, and still one of the top capacity grounds in the country—as the attendance of 78,599 in the match against Liverpool, in 1948, will testify.

Yes, Everton were among the pioneers of ground improvement and they kept up this reputation by being the first Football League club to try to beat the frost and ice bogy.

For many years club officials had been talking about means of preventing pitches becoming iced-up, but Everton were the first to install electrical equipment under the turf to prevent ice forming.

… continued from page 62.

Gordon West hailed from Blackpool not far up the coast,

his handling was perfect, he was calmer than most.

A popular goalie, the clubs number one,

after five hundred games it was time to move on.

Some wonderful strikers have played for our team,

the number one daddy was of course Dixie Dean.

Tom Lawton, Joe Royle, and big Andy Gray,

from north of the border, Alex Young joined the fray.

A will of the wisp, clever and graceful,

he was the vision of gold for the Goodison faithful.

Ed Wainwright, Nobby Feilding, and Ant McNamara,

the legendry Hickson and John Willie Parker.

Big Fergie was Scottish, fierce and aggressive,

he flattened opponents who were over possessive.

And the 'scallies' who foolishly entered his home,

must have feared for their lives, as he walked in alone.

Roy Vernon, a Taffy, tough as old leather,

swarthy, dark featured and light as feather.

He'd shoot down the wing and head towards goal,

his rivals were staggered by the dummies he sold.

Bob Latchford arrived in the year seventy four,

the club paid out thousands to make him secure.

Mackenzie and Sharpy, inventive, prolific,

Tony Cottee, Dave Johnston and Sheedy terrific.

DATES SPORTING AND DATA.

8th Sept 1937. WEDNESDAY EVENING THE 8th OF SEPTEMBER, 1937, WAS A POIGNANT ONE FOR THE FAMED Everton & England CENTRE-FORWARD — Dixie Dean — FOR ON THIS DATE HE WAS DISPLACED IN THE Everton SIDE TO PLAY Manchester City BY AN UP AND COMING YOUNGSTER NAMED Tom Lawton.

Dean, HOLDER OF THE DIVISION 1 SCORING RECORD WITH 60 GOALS IN SEASON 1927-28, WAS TO PLAY ONLY ONE MORE SENIOR GAME FOR THE GOODISON CLUB BEFORE HIS SUBSEQUENT TRANSFER TO Notts County.

YET THIS MERSEYSIDE IDOL BROUGHT A NEW TECHNIQUE AND ARTISTIC BRAND OF HEADING TO FOOTBALL THAT WILL ALWAYS REMAIN SYNONYMOUS WITH HIS NAME, WHICH WITH HIS PROLIFIC SCORING ABILITY WILL ALWAYS BE TALKED ABOUT WHENEVER FOOTBALL IS DISCUSSED.

W. R. DEAN

£111,000 IS THE WORLD'S TOP TRANSFER FEE

RECOGNISED as the world's highest transfer fee is the figure £111,000 paid for outside-right Julinho (Brazil) to Florence when he returned home to Palmeiras F.C.

Norway started international matches in 1908 and their first victory came ten years later.

Players who have been capped for more than one country include: Kubala (Barcelona) with Hungary, Czechoslovakia and Spain, and Di Stefano (Real Madrid) with Argentina, Colombia and Spain.

On this form, Everton are winners

And an Aussie star for Britain

JOHN WATKISS, 20-year-old Sydney soccer star, has accepted an offer to play for the English First Division club Nottingham Forest. He is the first Australian soccer player to receive such an offer. Notts Forest will pay him £25 a week and provide return air fares.

Watkiss, who stands 6 ft. 1 in. and weighs 13 st. 4 lb., is centre-forward for Canterbury-Marrickville, one of Sydney's leading first division clubs. Last season the club gained premiership honours in the Sydney competition. Watkiss has played for it since he was 16.

For some years football experts have hailed him as Australia's brightest soccer prospect. He shines in a variety of half-back and forward positions but prefers to play right-half.

Apia-Leichhardt centre-forward Leopold Baumgartner (formerly of F.K. Austria) says that Watkiss is the most promising player in Australia. He predicts that he will have a bright future in England. Canterbury coach Denis Adrigan, a former Hungarian player and coach, said that the youngster would be a success in any football team in the world.

Watkiss owes a lot to Baumgartner, who was captain-coach of Canterbury last season when the team won the competition. The former Austrian international devoted a great deal of time to developing Watkiss's natural talent. He also spent much time in teaching and helping two other young Canterbury forwards, John Warren and Brian Smith, both still in their teens. It is likely that these two will also receive offers from England in the near future.

Watkiss was born in Wolverhampton, England. His father, Joe, an employee of a British metal company, was transferred to the Sydney branch of the firm nine years ago. Joe, incidentally, used to play for Bilston.

John was enrolled as a pupil at Gardiner's Road Junior Technical High School in the Sydney suburb of Mascot. As a schoolboy he played rugby league football. When he left school at the age of 15 he started on his soccer career. His first team was Botany Methodists, one of the clubs in the strong Protestant Church Alliance, a vast nursery for Sydney soccer hopefuls.

He showed such ability in the game that Canterbury signed him on when he was 16 and he moved into First Division soccer after only a few matches in the lower grades.

… continued from page 64.

John Bailey a prankster and first rate left back,
boosted team spirits with his up to date crack.
Paul Bracewell, a great buy - vital cog in midfield,
made his debut at Wembley in the Charity Shield.

Andy King was a character, bubbly, good fun,
joined the Blues from 'The Hatters' for a reasonable sum.
There was Heathie and Dobbo and wing half John Hurst,
and fearless Mick Lyons many ego's he'd burst.

Johnny Morrisey, a tough lad, strong on the ball,
swopped allegiance with Anfield entered the Blues famous hall.
Tommy Wright also local, capped for England at school,
made his debut at nineteen was stylish and cool.

Tom Jones a great stalwart, known as simply T.E,
his career was in tatters when he damaged his knee.
Alex Parker from Falkirk classy and slick,
came South in the fifties was tremendously quick.

I'll mention Fred Pickering who missed out on his dream,
when his sidekick was chosen for the Cup Final team.
Mike Trebilcock, from Cornwall, was the hero that day,
Sheffield Wednesday were stung by his two goal display.

● Harry Catterick ... Manager of the Month for October last year when we took nine points out of ten, winning away games against Wolves and Coventry and toppling Stoke City 6-2 for our biggest win of the season. Harry is pictured receiving one of his prizes from the sponsors—a gallon bottle of Bell's Whisky. Cheers, Harry!

EVERTON F.C. 1959-60

Left to right: (Back row) T. Jones, K. Rea, A. Parker, A. Dunlop, J. Bramwell, M. Meagan, J. Tansey, G. Watson (Trainer); (Front row) A. Sanders, J. Harris, E. Thomas, D. Hickson, R. Collins, E. O'Hara B. Harris

… continued from page 66

'There's bound to be more Tom, that have slipped through the net,
so I'll scan through this scrapbook there'll be plenty I bet.
Ah!! here's Jimmy Gabriel all the way from Dundee,

cost a lot for a youngster, but he was worth the high fee.'

'And what about Temple and his Cup Final rocket?

If the goalie had touched it would have torn out his socket.

I remember quite clearly seeing the ball in full flight,

we drank half of London celebrating that night.

'Let's check a few more Tom, then we'll stop for a break,
my old eyes are struggling to keep me awake.
There's hundreds of players going back donkeys years,
who signed for the Toffees to enhance their careers.'

Brian Harris, Dave Unsworth are two I recall,
both had their moments of fame in 'the Hall'.
Denis Stevens arrived in March sixty two,
won a cup medal for Bolton then converted to blue.

And last but not least, from old Shrewsbury Town,
Cyril Lello was loyal, never let the team down.
Well lad, I'm ready for a smoke and a spell,
I could murder a cuppa - give your Grandma a yell.

'My wages were £12 per week'

ALBERT STUBBINS

"Who is this 'rid' you keep telling them to get!"

Bob Paisley—40 years at Liverpool

McDermott, Hughes, Neal, Kennedy, Thompson and Clemence

Don't forget the Reds

'Gramps you've not mentioned the Red's for a while,
and there's plenty of Bill's stuff over here in a pile.'
Dan nodded his head - he'd been trying to stall,
most of their players, he could easily recall.

He tried to play down what the Red's had achieved,
but their record spoke volumes, so he had to concede.
The success they'd attained since Bill Shankly took charge,
left the Blues in the shadow, like a slow moving barge.

Dan opened Bill's diary scanned everyone's name,
and noted the positions they played in the game.
Cyril Sidlow, in goal, Jones and Shepherd full back,
Laurie Hughes and Bill Spicer, Bob Paisley, mid pack,
Jimmy Payne on the wing, Kevin Baron inside,
Stubbins with Balmer, Billy Liddell played wide.

It was during the fifties 'the Pool' hit a low,
they lost their momentum, the team were too slow.
Don Welsh and Phil Taylor tried their best to improve
but the Reds near the bottom were unable to move.

The fans were disheartened by the Red's sorry state,
someone was needed to improve the club's fate.
The country's top coaches were scanned for the post,
Bill Shankly was favourite, he impressed more than most.

The city was buzzing when 'the Pool' signed their man,
a no nonsense Scot to lead the Red clan.
His profile was perfect, credentials top draw,
the only way forward was to follow his law.

Oh,oh, oh, ho,
Worra a referee, worra referee, worra referee,
Oh. oh. oh, oh worra a referee,
The linesmen's hit the heavy stuff,
and were kicking off at three.

GUINNESS
For winners
Red cards for sinners

The great Bill Shankly

When Shanks arrived at Anfield the club were in a mess,

he brought a brand of football and system to impress.

His scouts were drafted far and wide to harvest local talent,

they had to have a certain trait be keen and fit and gallant.

The first squad he assembled was quite a decent team,

success was round the corner as they eased their way upstream.

Eventually in sixty two their efforts were rewarded,

they won the league convincingly and medals were awarded.

From strength to strength the Red's progressed

under Shanklys turbulent reign,

the cup and league was won with ease, and they were never out the frame.

Unfortunately the Blue's had slipped and struggled for a while,

they had to wait 'til sixty three to make supporters smile.

Shank's quotes and sense of humour, were always headline news,

he was revered by half of Liverpool who simply shared his views.

Ambition was his goal in life, popular with the press,

he treated every game the same, like a master move in chess.

Big Yeatsy was colossal, while Roger hunted goals,

'The Saint' a canny schemer, matched Cally's ball control.

Keeper Tommy Lawrence, called the flying pig,

and Emlyn Hughes a crazy horse, long legs and heart as big.

Neal and Chrissie Lawler, Brian Hall and Terry Mac,

Phil and Peter Thompson, Tosh leading the attack.

Tommy Smith a legend, who ruled the roost with pride,

his tackles were ferocious, even hard men tried to hide.

...The Boot Room Boys...

…continued from page 72.

Shanks also formed a boot room, for tactics to discuss,

the squads he chose were on the ball, bad practice swiftly crushed.

They'd plot the fall of visitors with a dram to ease their taste,

this cosy spec was known to all as 'the gaffer's favourite base.'

As years passed by Bill shocked the fans when he made a tough decision,

he reckoned that the time had come to start a new transition.

Top scouts were called to earn their corn, scan every single game,

as stars moved on, young blood arrived, to replace and seek their fame.

The popular Jimmy Melia, joined Wolves in sixty four,

he gave his best repeatedly and pleased the Anfield core,

Milne and Willie Stevenson, Geoff Strong and Gerry Byrne,

made their way to pastures new, never to return.

The exodus continued, just like a marathon race,

those who lapsed before the end, were deemed to lack the pace.

The Saint and Bobby Graham and 'big man' Ronny Yeats,

well known stars who left the Reds and rightly classed as greats.

Famous names and legends, departed from the club,

including Kevan Keegan and Dave the super sub.

Clemence, Rushie, Souness - Heighway, Jimmy Case,

Lindsey, Alan Kennedy left the family base.

'Keegan's better than ever'

KENNY'S KING OF THE KOP

EVERTON, LIVERPOOL SEEK STAR PLAYERS

Managers In Scotland

AT FALKIRK

By LESLIE EDWARDS

City football fans rejoice! Both Everton and Liverpool clubs destined, it seemed, to start the season without new faces (and, more important, new feet) are both making moves to change that dismal situation.

All going well it looks as hough we shall have some notable newcomers at one or ther, or both, camps between ow and the start of the season August 22) and the sooner the etter.

…continued from page 74.

Though Shanks had set the pattern, his training staff agreed,

once a player lost his pace there was nothing guaranteed.

Bill sanctioned many clean sweeps throughout his colourful reign,

but he'd always spot a glittering gem hidden in the grain.

Headline news that Shank's had quit was a bombshell from the press,

the Blue half were delighted, the Red's weighed down with stress.

Rumours drenched the grapevine, that Bill had lost his fire,

'The Echo' claimed he'd reached his peak and was ready to retire.

It was no surprise Shank's right hand man would step into his shoes,

Bob Paisley was the perfect choice, he shared his gaffer's views.

Bill realised his time was up and reached a life's ambition,

he'd stabilised a sinking ship and restored a proud tradition.

Young Tom was sitting quietly, absorbing every word,

everything his grandpa said, were tales he'd never heard.

Of course he knew that Shankly, had been treated like a God,

he was down to earth and spoke his mind, well respected by his squad.

Catterick was a different fish, the opposite to Shank's,

'it was just like chalk and cheese the way 'Cat's always closed his ranks.'

Charisma, he was short of - old fashioned in a way,

some reckoned he was aloof at times, yet he got his team to play.

The Captain from the North
Phil Taylor

'King Kenny' with Bruce
Grobbelaar – Double Delight.

All smiles. . .Bob Paisley and Ian
Callaghan.

A city united

The all Mersey Cup Final 1984 produced such a feeling of togetherness in the city, that the clubs posed, side by side, for this specially commissioned picture before the FA Cup Final of '86 when the two teams met again.

Merseyside's two great football clubs, always close, had never been closer.

And this remarkable picture reflected the unity on Merseyside that today — is even closer still.

Taking stock.

Just after lunch we settled down with our priceless information,
the contents taken from the loft were viewed with admiration.
The Driscoll's gift, I was pleased to note, had passed along the line,
the writing was impeccable and neatly done in rhyme.

We enjoyed the happy memories, spread thirty years or more,
it felt we'd entered Aladdin's cave with a genie on the door.
Programmes we stacked neatly - some dated fifty eight,
for drawings, scrap books, ticket stubs I'd found a special crate.

The notes and observations I read with glowing pride,
it felt as though our Bill and Jim were standing by my side.
The weekend went so quickly, young Tom was sad to go,
he'd learnt so much in those few days of things he'd never know.

The house was quiet, the tele on, we were back in our routine,
with Mary glued to Corrie Street, I closed my eyes to dream.
The last two days had fired my blood and revived a latent passion,
with loads of games on Sky T.V, ensured I had my ration.

'This is the life' I said out loud as Mary glanced my way,
a double dram of Scotch I sank, to toast another day.
With news at ten switched off at last, my flock looked so inviting,
I hit the hay in record time, just like a bolt of lightening.

"It's all that mouse you ate last night is sending you doo lally,
I haven't had a wink of sleep, you dirty blue-nosed scally."

Too much cheese or what like!!

That night I had the strangest dream so vivid and prophetic,

my brain was working overtime I felt fit and energetic.

I was wandering around one sunny day, full of the joys of spring,

my favourite team was on my mind, I could hear the songbirds sing.

Who'd score first? How many goals? What would the outcome be?

I'd settle for two precious points, but made up if it's three.

But when I climbed up Everton Brow my world was blown away,

Goodison Park had disappeared, replaced by mounds of clay.

I felt like Dickie Lewis, suspended without kecks,

when someone tapped my shoulder, I dropped my reading specs.

I recognized our Billy, who'd been a fervent Red,

he'd popped his clogs six years ago - his missus found him dead.

He didn't say a word at first but lead me by my arm,

we made our way to Anfield Road, amazed that I was calm.

Everything was eerie, as I neared my rival's ground,

like Everton's Shrine, the place was bare, not a relic to be found.

'Follow me' our Billy said, as we joined the passing crowd,

without a hint of blue or red, yet the noise was very loud.

In Scottie Road the streets were packed like an Orange Lodge procession,

the crowd had merged in single file with patience and discretion.

I tried to fathom out the score, the place was chocka block,

Bill read my thoughts then pointed to the famous Princess dock.

And when I saw the height and length, I couldn't move an inch,

I wiped my eyes, then gasped for breath, and gave my cheek a pinch.

GEOFF. TWENTYMAN

IAN ST. JOHN
Liverpool F.C.
Young, small and
stocky centre-forward
with exceptional skill
and speed off the
mark. A tireless
worker who is very
difficult to stop.

John Morrissey plays his third
League game for Liverpool
at Sunderland, on Saturday.
Normally he is a left winger.
Now he is being tried on the
right.

HICKSON

COLLINS

ALAN A'COURT
A Liverpool F.C.
player who appeared
for England in World
Cup matches against
Brazil, Austria and
Russia. Played for a
Schools' Week XI v.
Pegasus and repre-
sented Lancashire
Grammar Schools.
Is a keen coach.

Johnny Wheeler, whose
first game as captain of
Liverpool will be against
Grimsby Town at Anfield
on Saturday

…continued from page 80.

The largest stadium in the world, on the Mersey had been built,
it stretched across the River's girth on massive iron stilts.
I gazed around this awesome sight, rooted to the spot,
then followed Bill up marble stairs until we reached the top.

A pair of gates were open, with a fellow standing guard,
he asked if I was visiting, then slipped a yellow card.
We ambled down a passageway that led into a square,
everyone seemed full of joy, like going to a fair.

There were pubs on every corner, theatres, posh hotels,
shopping malls with cinemas, top clothes for clientele.
I clocked a railway station, called the Heavenly link,
it carried souls from either side, those lingering on the brink.

The crowds began arriving, the atmosphere was great,
there must have been a hundred thou passed through the golden gate.
When everyone was seated, the band began to play,
Anfield Road, then Z cars, were popular songs that day.

The fans joined in the banter, as each player showed his pace,
for Scouse United's opening game, keen rivals they would face.
Mancunian Caledonian, from the city down the way,
they boasted winning cups galore and would show us how to play.

The highlight of the day arrived, the time was three o'clock,
Elisha was in goal that day, as solid as a rock.
Full backs Warnie Cresswell, and fearless Tommy Smith,
Harvey next to Brian Labone - Joe Mercer was no myth.

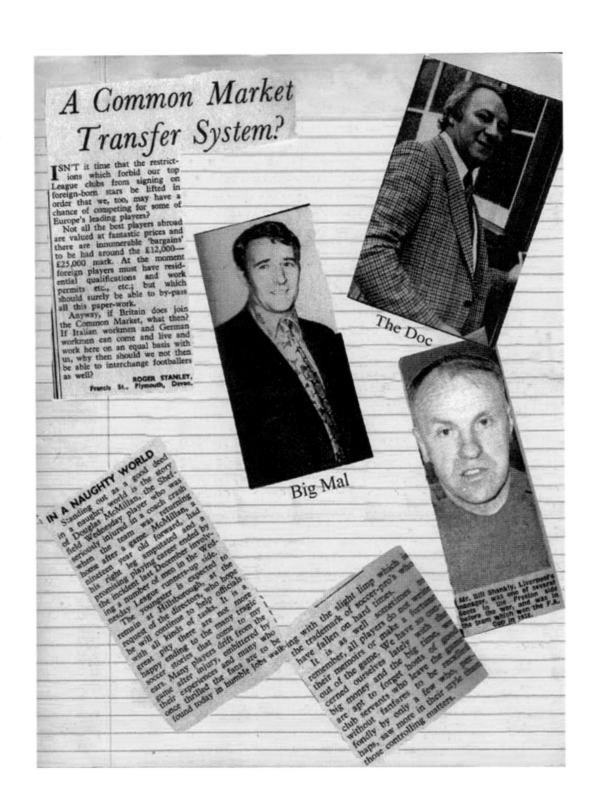

A Common Market Transfer System?

ISN'T it time that the restrictions which forbid our top League clubs from signing on foreign-born stars be lifted in order that we, too, may have a chance of competing for some of Europe's leading players?

Not all the best players abroad are valued at fantastic prices and there are innumerable 'bargains' to be had around the £12,000—£25,000 mark. At the moment foreign players must have residential qualifications and work permits etc., etc.; but which should surely be able to by-pass all this paper-work.

Anyway, if Britain does join the Common Market, what then? If Italian workmen and German workmen can come and live and work here on an equal basis with us, why then should we not then be able to interchange footballers as well?

ROGER STANLEY,
Francis St., Plymouth, Devon.

The Doc

Big Mal

IN A NAUGHTY WORLD

Standing out as a good deed in a naughty world is the story of Douglas McMillan, the Sheffield Wednesday player who was seriously injured in a coach crash when the team was returning home after a game. McMillan, a nineteen year old forward, had his right leg amputated and a promising playing career ended by the incident last December involving a number of men in the Wednesday League runners-up side.

The youngster is expected to remain at Hillsborough, at the request of the directors, who hope he will continue to help officials with all kinds of tasks. It is a great pity there are not more happy endings to the many tragic soccer stories that come to my ears. Many players drift from the game after injury, embittered by their experiences and many who once thrilled the fans are to be found today in humble jobs.

...king with the slight limp which... the trademark of soccer-pro's wh... have fallen on hard times.

It is as well sometimes... remember, all players do not w... their memoirs or make a fortu... out of the game. We have so... cerned ourselves lately with... big money and the big time,... are apt to forget those of... club servants who leave the... without fanfares to be rec... fondly by only a few who,... haps, saw more in their style th... those controlling matters.

Mr. Bill Shankly, Liverpool's manager, was one of several Scots to the war, and was in before the team which won the F.A. Cup in 19...

…continued from page 82.

The Golden Vision down the flanks, with the fantastic Billy Liddell,
Dalglish, St John created goals, King Dixie ruled the middle.
And when our opponent's team was named, they were treated with respect,
for after all, it was just a game, no anger to reflect.

Bert Trautmann was their goalie, a brave and fearless keeper,
with a broken neck he carried on, and thwarted every sweeper.
Johnny Carey played at right back, with captain Roger Byrne,
he would have been an English great there was nothing more to learn.

Brilliant Duncan Edwards, towered in mid field,
with tenacious Keane and Colin Bell, they formed a solid shield.
Their forward line was awesome, attacking was the game,
whoever had to choose these five, spent hours trying to name.

Georgie Best, Denis Law and the amazing Cantona,
with Bobby Charlton's lethal boot, it was the best by far.
Finally when Wayne appeared a roar rang out like thunder,
he waved his fist, saluted fans determined not to blunder.

This was his home, where he belonged despite the opposition,
with a trannie mop of dark brown hair he was ready for the mission.
The game became a classic show, the second half dramatic,
it finished up two goals a piece with everyone ecstatic.

Families were together, refreshments cost them nowt,
no super stars on massive wage or agents were about.
Tugging shirts and diving, were treated with contempt,
and in ninety minutes fiercely fought, there wasn't one attempt.

BOBBY CHARLTON
Manchester United and England

The Man With Goals in Both Feet
Kevin Baron

I NEVER imagined I would see
the day when Spanish soccer
officials would get worried—because of the possibility of some of
their top-class players being lured
abroad.

It has always been the other
way round — until the recent
Italian big - money spree. After
Internazionale secured Barcelona's Luis Suarez (for, it is
rumoured, at least £10,000), such names
as Luis Del Sol, Francisco Gento
and Joaquin Peiro were linked as
next most likely to journey to
sunny Italia.

The Spanish Football Federa-
tion have, accordingly, just issued
a directive advising their member
clubs not to allow their best players to move abroad. "Remember
the World Cup is next year—and
we will require all of our best
men to represent us in Chile."

Looks like no British are not
the only country who will need to
go cap in hand to the Italians
asking, "May we have our men
back please? for the 1962 World
Cup finals?"

Italy's hero

LORENZO BUFFON, Inter-
nazionale and Italy's national
goalkeeper and captain, has just
been voted Italy's Top Player for
1960-61. He is undoubtedly one
of the most artistic goalkeepers in
Europe and one of the most fearless. A daring dive at the feet of
England skipper Johnny Haynes
in the international in Rome last
May, resulted in his receiving a
broken nose (see my photograph
this week).

For those who are interested
previous Italian Footballers of
the Year have been:
1951-52: Parola; 1952-53: Lor-
enzi; 1953-54: Boniperti; 1956-
Ferrario; 1955-56: Virgili; 1956-
57: Bean; 1957-58: John Charles;
1958-59: Nicole; 1959-60: Sivori.

"Why do you ask me how we got
on only when we lose?"

…continued from page 84.

Across the pitch famed managers strolled, all were young and happy,
Matt Busby led the entourage, Shanks looking sharp and snappy.
Clive Britton, Harry Catterick - Bob Paisley, Tony Book,
Howard Kendall, Wilf McGuinness - Tom Docherty's knowing look.

Flamboyant Mal was next in line with his usual panache,
large cigar, fedora hat, outspoken often brash.
Joe Fagan walked with Ron Moran, Roy Evans tagged along,
Scot Duncan, Jimmy Murphy - Graham Souness fit and strong.

Joe Royle, and Ronnie Atkinson, sharing latest crack,
Ron glancing over shoulder in case someone stabbed his back.
Genial Gerard Houllier, in double breasted suit,
trying to wind bold Rafa up, who didn't give a hoot.

And then the man himself appeared, looking mighty pleased,
Fergie, with his fellow Scots, taking in the breeze.
King Kenny on his left side, Moysie on the right,
he'd sorted out the referee who'd vanished out of sight.

With everyone in jovial mood, fine music was expected,
all kinds of passionate songs were sung and nobody objected.
Quite suddenly the speakers squawked, a voice began to utter,
'Worrabout me party piece,' it sounded like a splutter.
The roof was raised, the crowd joined in, they had the greatest fun,
their vocal chords were exercised as the mascot sang his pun.

LIVERPOOL PERSONALITIES

CRÖSSLEY

JONES

SPICER

SAUNDERS

HUGHES

MALONEY

BARON

SMYTH

PAYNE

SMITH

LIDDELL

…continued from page 86.

'Last night we had a doo,

From one o'clock 'til two,

We had some German kippers from the Rhine.

''FROM THE RHINE.''

The kippers they were wooden,

So we had some cast iron puddin'

And the smell of the kippers,

killed the cat.'

The afternoon drew to a close, with a rapturous ovation,

it hadn't cost a penny piece nor fear of exploitation.

And as I left my comfy seat and glanced across the bay,

I could see as far as Blackpool tower, clear as night from day.

Skyscrapers blotted Birkenhead's fine buildings tall and bold,

it looked like China's new Shanghai and worth its weight in gold.

Three Graces were so splendid, Cathedrals to the right,

the Liver Birds were half a sleep beneath a cloudless night.

SCOUSE UNITED

E Scott

W Cresswell   T Smith

C Harvey   B Labone   J Mercer

A Young   K Daglish   D Dean   I St.John   W Liddell

R Charlton   W Rooney   Cantona   D Law   G Best

C Bell   D Edwards   R Keane

R Byrne   J Carey

B Trautmam

MANCUNIAN CALEDONIA

…continued from page 88.

I didn't see our Billy go, nor glimpse his smiling face,

one minute he was by my side then vanished without trace.

And then I heard a familiar howl ringing in my ears,

the same old tone had never changed in fifty sodden years.

'Gerr up you lazy so and so, the kids convoy's been and gone,

Snellie's show is over - Shaun Styles is coming on.'

I tugged the duvet from my head, my mind in disarray,

'What's happened to my pride and joy' I asked in sheer dismay.

'Has Goodison Park and Anfield gone, were they mentioned on the news?

She had that cocky toothless grin some Reds reserve for Blue's.

'It's all that mouse you ate last night is sending you doo lally,

I haven't had a wink of sleep, you dirty blue -nosed scally.'

It's time you acted sensibly and stopped halucinatin'

and go to sleep like most folk do instead of postulatin'

By now you should have ditched those dreams,

like a youngster would have done.

But she fails to see the way I feel about this harmless fun.

C. SIDLOW (Liverpool)
Welsh international goalkeeper is one of the
capable custodians in the First Division

W. SHANKLY
PRESTON N.E.

A. STEVENSON
Everton

LOUIS BIMPSON

…continued from page 90

My better half was right of course, she's had me decked for ages,

I quickly scoffed two hard boiled eggs then scanned the local pages.

I couldn't find a word in print to back my crazy story,

that Scouse United played in town with style and fame and glory.

Then suddenly some breaking news stopped Mary in mid - stream,

an arsonist was on the run - down the East Lancs Road it seemed.

Wrigleys famous factory was reputedly on fire,

investors rushed to sell their shares, fearing Fergie would retire.

The rumour was a 'wind up,' that began in dear old Huyton,

it swept across the Mersey Bar, and even reached New Brighton.

Summary

As Father Time sneaks slowly by we start another season,

I'm still the same old doddering fool at odds with sense and reason.

Mary says I'll never change, it's in the genes she reckons,

I must agree, she's usually right, as I wait my dreams to beckon.

On a final note I'd like to say this trip has been a pleasure,

Memories of those epic games will stay around forever.

The scrapbooks tell a story on every faded page,

of how our heroes played the game in a less material age.

Mister Wang's verdict

Now the time has come to speculate, about the bladder and its writing.
Sadly Mister Wang has died, what did he find exciting?
We can now reveal the mystery he solved with basic knowledge,
it's just a famous proverb from a Chinese culture college.

This spiritual gift, destined to float,
Across oceans and deserts, however remote.
It completed its journey brought joy to mankind,
Helped nations to progress in soul and in mind.